This book belongs to

....

....

Published in 2021 by Alligator Products Ltd.
Cupcake is an imprint of Alligator Products Ltd.
2nd Floor, 314 Regents Park Road, London N3 2JX

Written by Christine Barrett
Illustrated by Julie Clough

Printed in China.1745

Animal Fashion Parade

cupcake

Welcome to the animal fashion parade.
Look at the amazing outfits they have made!

Ballerina bunnies dance
as the audience cheer.

A pig in pink pants, that really won't do.

A blue feather boa draped over a hairy gnu!

A red spotty coat for an elegant cat

Can you see where she has left her hat?

Henry Hippo can't decide which hat to wear.

Meanwhile, a little spider gets ready to give him a scare!

Zebra's coat is so stylish, he looks very cool.

Snooty Fox has socks,

jumper and hat

– all made of wool!

There is chaos backstage,
and it's looking a mess,
for Panda can't find
her favourite dress.

Two pretty parrots watch,

quietly having a preen.

It is the best fashion show

they have ever seen!

Four woolly boots for Fluffy the sheep

who finishes her act with a jump and a leap.

Puppy was sleeping backstage on a chair,
so pyjamas are all that she has to wear!

Cow's polka dot pants are quite a surprise!

Mole's sunglasses keep the lights out of his eyes.

Everyone gathers backstage to help poor Giraffe.

For with such a long neck,

she needs more than one scarf.

Flamingo is
dressed to go
to a fabulous ball.

Mouse peeps over her sarong.

She is just too small!

Elephant looks quite regal
in her glistening gold crown.

But ooops, she's tripped over
and now everyone's fallen down!

That is the end of the
fashion parade... can you
remember which outfit
each animal made?

Goodbye!